Wilma had a creepy-crawly.
She put it in the bath.

Wilma called Dad.

"Get it out," said Wilf.

"Ugh! I couldn't," said Dad.

Wilf called Mum.

"Get it out," said Wilf.

"Ugh! I couldn't," said Mum.

Wilma called Chip.

"Get it out," said Wilf.

"Ugh! I couldn't," said Chip.

Wilf called Biff.

"Get it out," said Wilma.

"Ugh! I couldn't," said Biff.

Everyone called Kipper.

"Get it out," said Wilf.

"Easy!" said Kipper.